ROLF HEIMANN'S

BRAIN BUSTING BONANZA

Welcome to my biggest book ever of all-new mazes, puzzles, spottos, conundrums, quizzes, teasers, stumpers and bafflers!

I was seven years old the first time I got lost in a maze.
It was a real maze, made from hedges.

Every turn I took either led to a dead end or to another fork.
I feared that I was stuck there forever, and I wondered how long
it would be before I starved to death. Then I suddenly found myself
at the exit—and this wonderful moment made it all worthwhile.

Me!

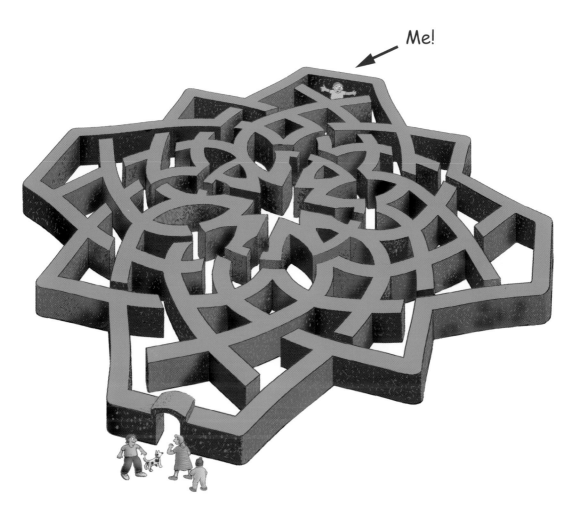

The moment of discovery—when you find your way out of a maze,
find a solution to a tricky puzzle, or work out the answer to a baffling
brain-buster—is the reason why people all over the world enjoy doing
puzzles and mazes. And one thing is for sure: nobody has ever starved
to death in any of *my* mazes!

(But you might starve if you try to do all the puzzles
and mazes in this bumper book without a break!)

These equations show you the value of Schnoponian fruit.

1. Gift-giving In the galaxy of Schnopos III, it is very important that diplomats give each other gifts of equal value. Are the gifts being offered here equal?

2. Fruit platter Arrange these platters in order of their value.

1.

2.

3.

4.

5.

3. Lost sock One of the diplomats has lost a tentacle sock. Which model does he have to buy?

6.

SANTA GLOW

ROYAL MARK

MOON KING

PENTO WALKER

TENTAC LE JOY

ASTRO NIGHT

YELLOW MOOD

RED STAR

SATURN SPRING

MOON BERRY

MARTIAN TWIRL

CLASSIC KIRNER

4. Star-crossed snake
Help the snake find its way
to the nest below.

5. Giant leaf
Only one of the four caterpillars will be able to reach the giant leaf. Which one? (They can only walk on the yellow paths.)

6. Pillars of society
These caterpillars only like the company of their own kind. Which one of them doesn't belong?

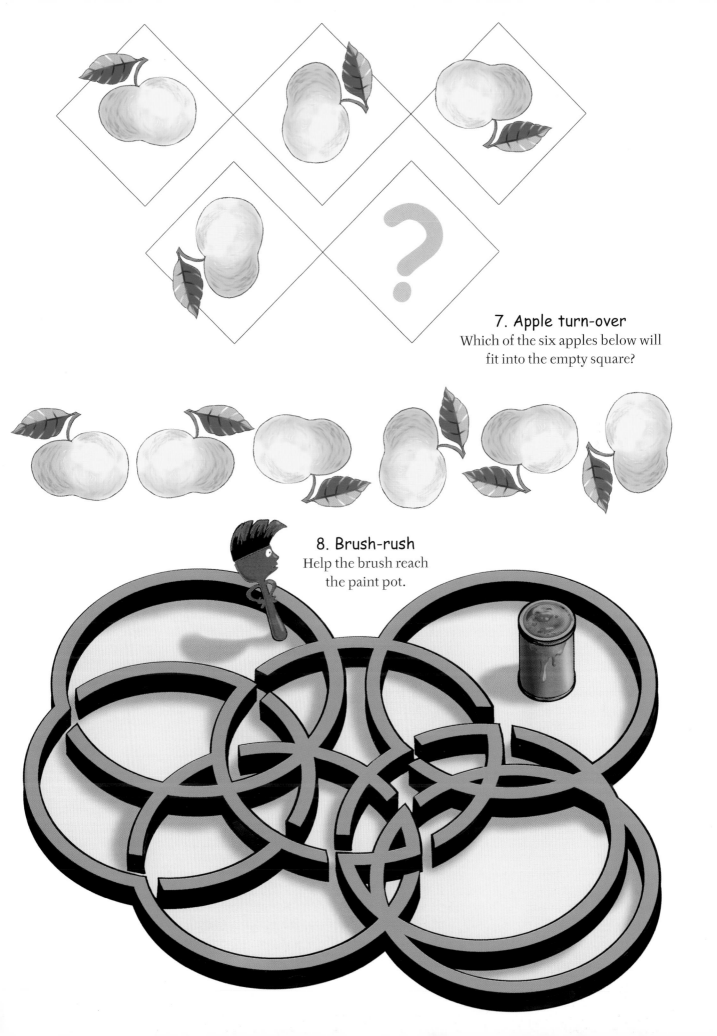

7. Apple turn-over

Which of the six apples below will fit into the empty square?

8. Brush-rush

Help the brush reach the paint pot.

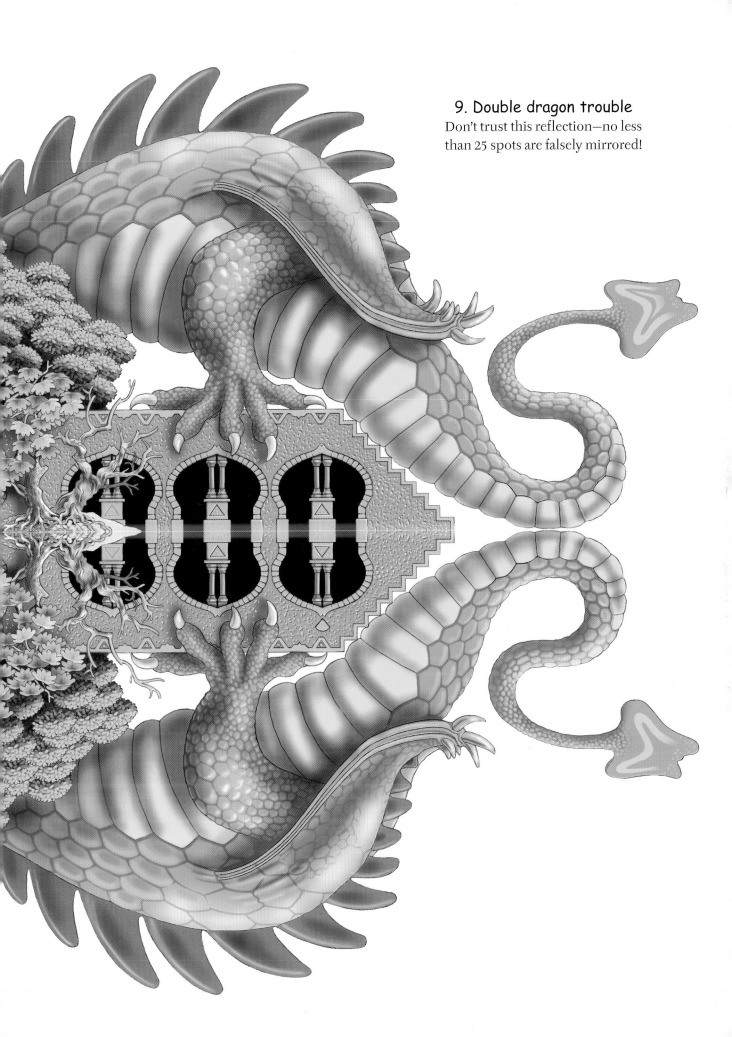

9. Double dragon trouble
Don't trust this reflection—no less than 25 spots are falsely mirrored!

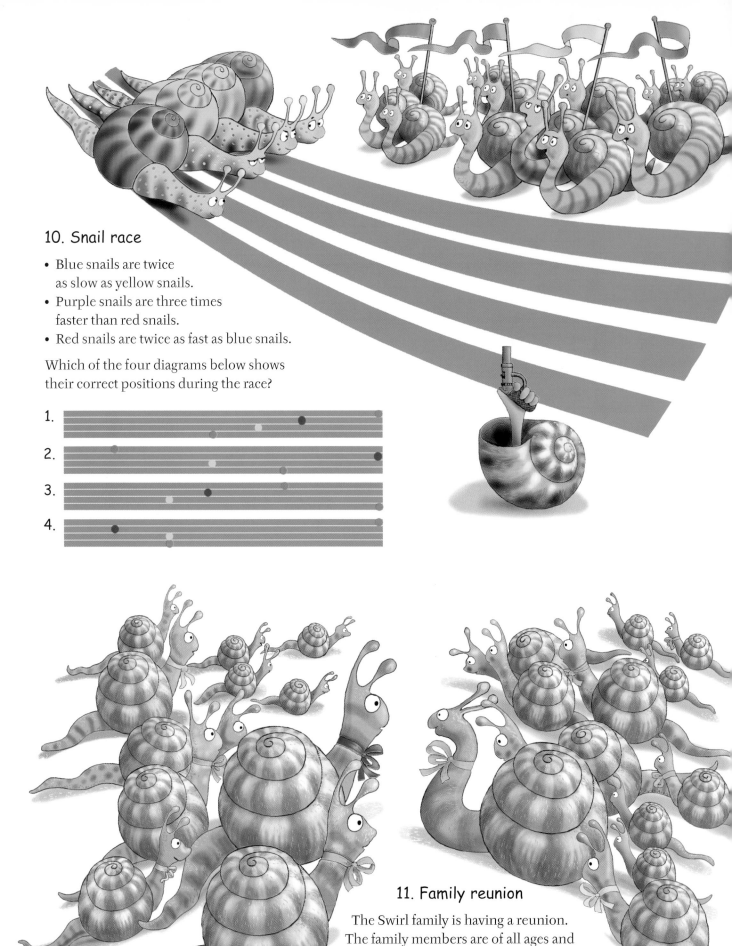

10. Snail race

- Blue snails are twice as slow as yellow snails.
- Purple snails are three times faster than red snails.
- Red snails are twice as fast as blue snails.

Which of the four diagrams below shows their correct positions during the race?

1.

2.

3.

4.

11. Family reunion

The Swirl family is having a reunion. The family members are of all ages and sizes, but one is definitely an outsider.

Which one and why?

12. Three-in-a-row
Find three-in-a-row of the following things:

Fish
Insects
Things with stripes
Things with dots

There is one picture left over. Which one?

13. Odd one out
Who or what is the odd one out?

14. Copied keys
Copies have been made of five of the six colored keys—which one was forgotten?

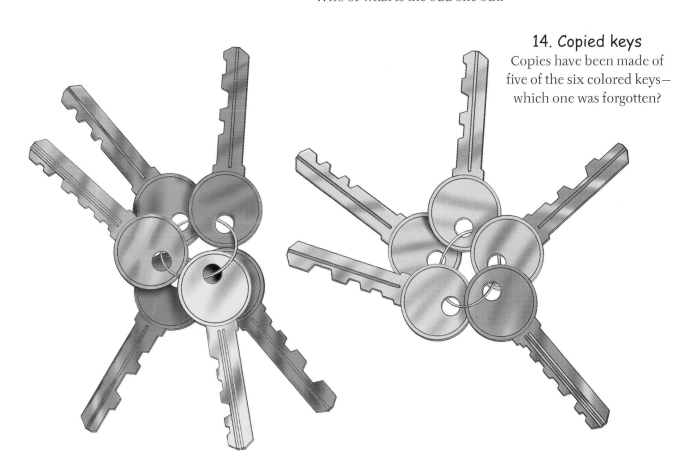

15. Apple snakes

Before the snakes got their hands on them, there were four green, four yellow and four red apples. What color are the apples inside the purple snake?

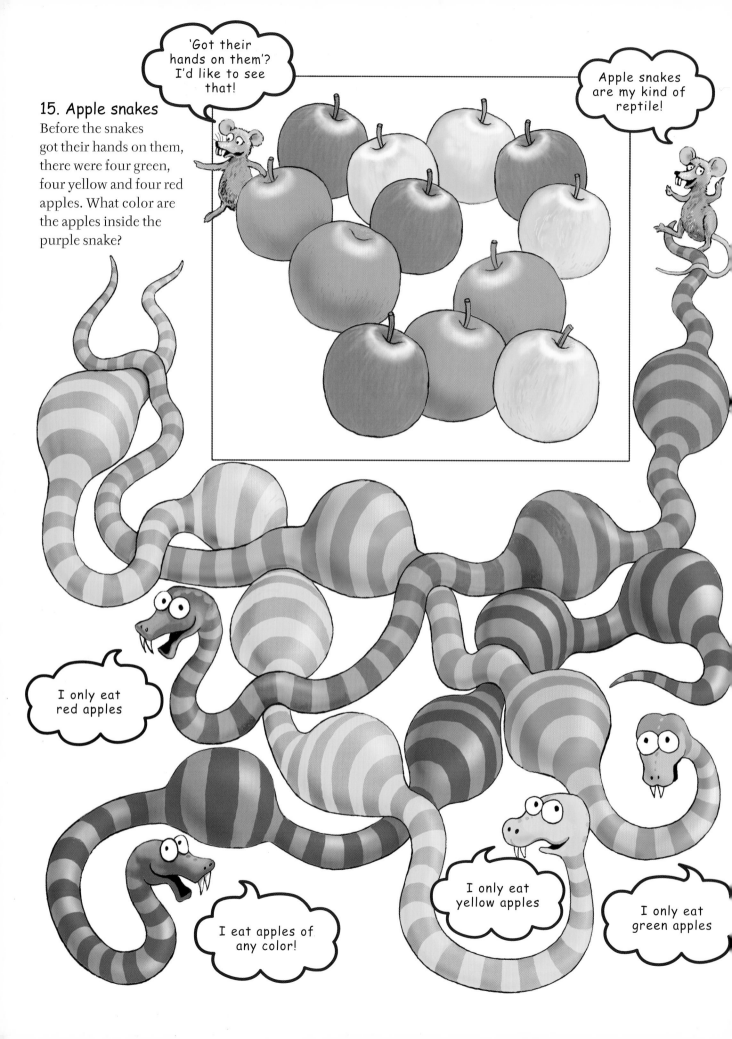

16. Out of reach
The only way for the mouse to reach the cheese is through the maze.

17. Butterfly friends

This butterfly is looking for a friend that is exactly like itself in every detail.

Which one could it be?

18. Pilot error

The Air Marshall is outraged! One of the
Red Squadron planes in the flying formation
is not exactly the same as the others.

Which one?

19. Double-checking double-deckers

When the pilots of the Yellow Squadron hear that
the Air Marshall is in a bad mood, they quickly check
their own planes. Uh oh!

Which one doesn't match...?

20. Day-dreamers
Have you ever noticed that sometimes clouds look like animals?

Spot at least a dozen here!

21. Fantastic faces

Trees—and even houses—often look like they have faces.

How many faces can you spot among these trees and houses?

22. House cat Which one of the cats below lives at number 5?

23. Cat and mouse
How did the mouse escape through the maze?

24. Special delivery
The brown parcel has to be delivered to a yellow house with a red roof and four chimneys.

Which number is the house?

25. Flower arrangement
The flowerbox is for the house that already has an identical arrangement.

Which house does it belong to?

26. Cat city!
How many cats are there?

Here's a hint: double the number of houses, then subtract the number of dogs you see.

27. Golden delicious

Why settle for little green apples when there's a ripe red one waiting?

Try to reach it without stepping over any lines.

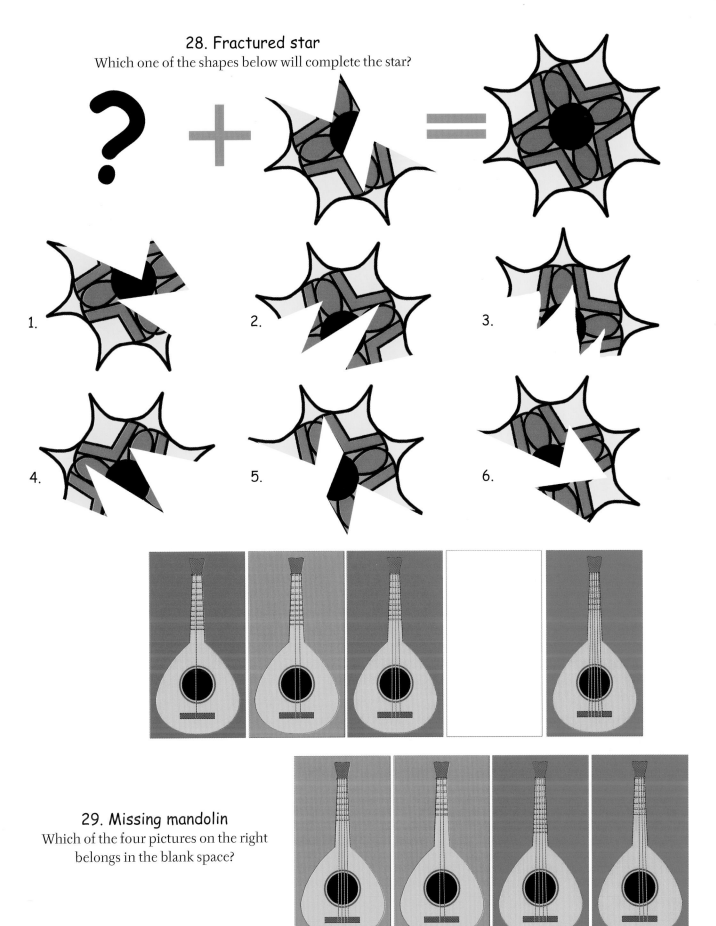

28. Fractured star
Which one of the shapes below will complete the star?

1.
2.
3.
4.
5.
6.

29. Missing mandolin
Which of the four pictures on the right belongs in the blank space?

1.
2.
3.
4.

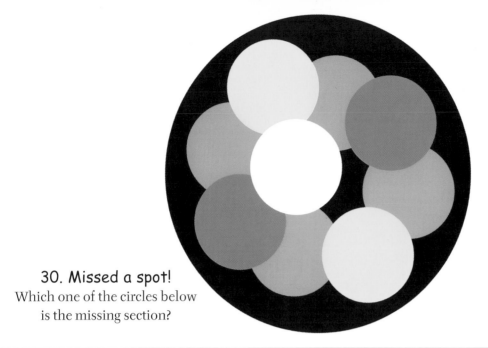

30. Missed a spot!
Which one of the circles below
is the missing section?

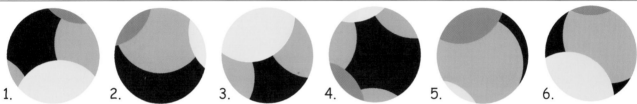

1.　　2.　　3.　　4.　　5.　　6.

31. Through the butterfly
Go in one antenna and out the other!

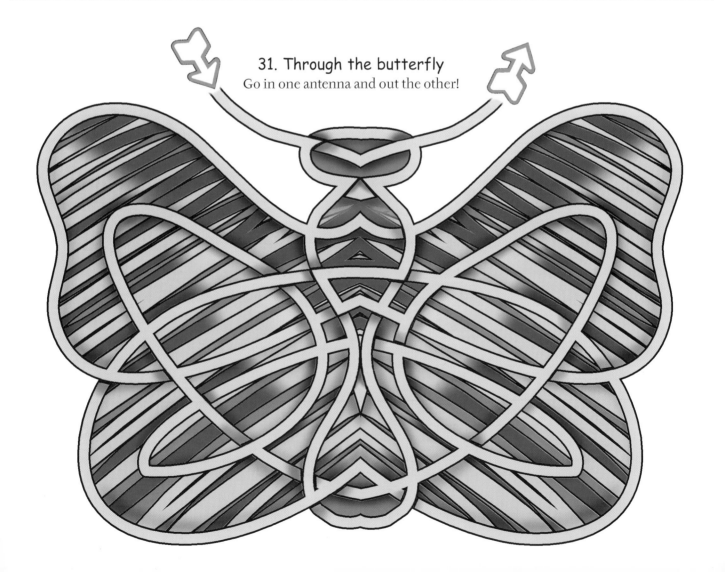

32. Apple-loving grub
Help the grub find
its way to the apple.

33. Tree of life
If you think that the tree in the center is symmetrical,
you're mistaken! Find three spots where it isn't...

34. Starry, starry jungle

Find your way from left to right.

35. Magic mandala
Find your way out from the center,
traveling only on the white lines.

36. Odd one out Which of the pictures above doesn't belong?

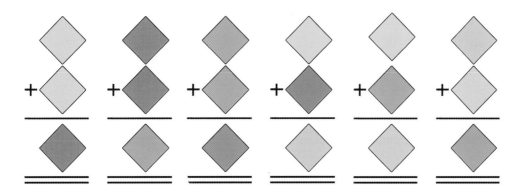

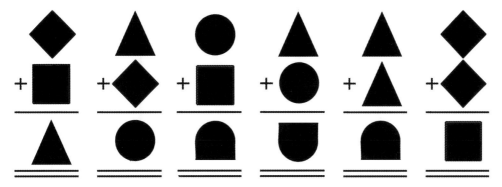

37. Color code Work out what number each color represents.

38. Shady deals In this puzzle, each shape represents a number.

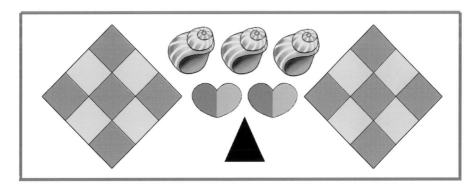

39. Odd objects Each object stands for a number.

40. All together now Using the values above, you'll see that the items in the little box add up to three. But what do the items in the big box add up to?

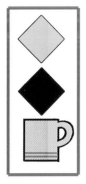

41. Odd one out

One of the items on the left doesn't belong.

Which one?

42. Vanishing violin case

Help the musician reach her violin case.

43. Notable error

In the notation of music, each note has a certain value (as shown here), and each bar must contain the same total.

full note	1/2	1/4	1/8	1/16

Check whether there is a mistake in one of the four bars below.

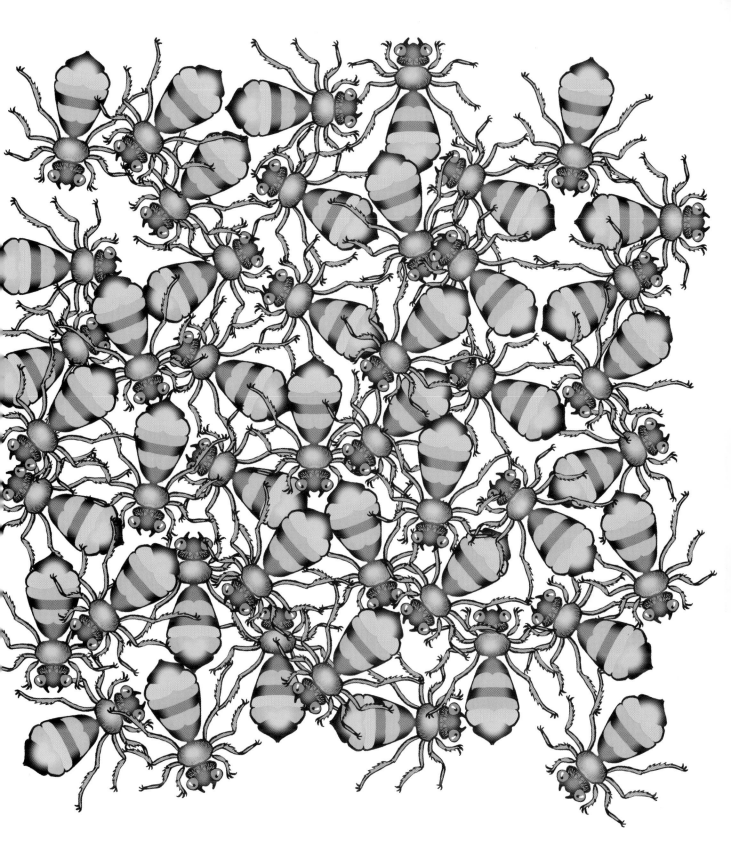

44. Spiders' nest

Scientists know that there are always more female honey spiders than male ones. Is the honey spider on the right male or female? (They're hard to tell apart, but they are definitely different.)

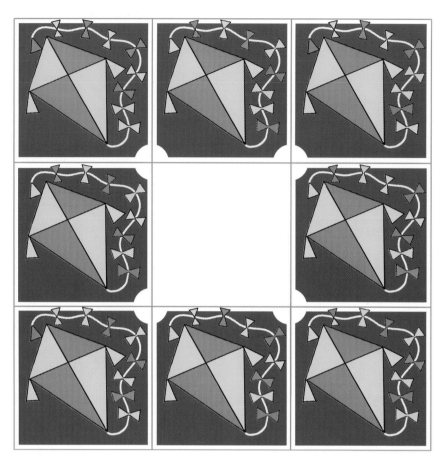

45. Colored kites Which of the 12 pictures below fits into the blank space?
(Hint: look at the sequence of colors on the tail!)

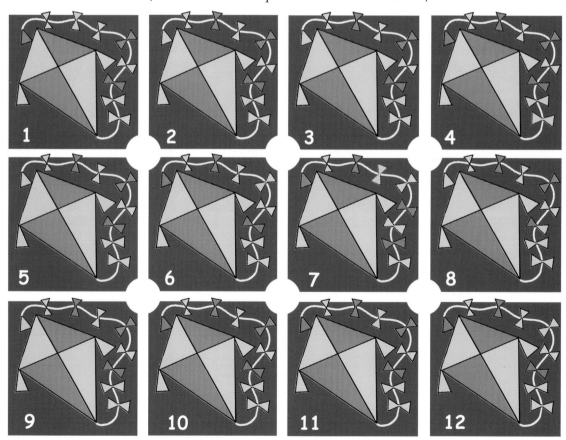

46. Giddy geckos
Only three of the 64 geckos are able to reach the crown in the center.

Which ones are they?

(Hint: It's the three geckos who look different to the others!)

47. Kite-flying competition
Only those who have dressed in the same colors as their kites are allowed to take part.

Are there are any children who should be disqualified?

48. Personal judgement
A special prize goes to the child who has dressed most like their kite.

(Warning: there's no correct answer. It's not easy being a judge, is it?!)

7lbs

2.5lbs

3lbs

49. Super balloon
Red balloons can lift 7 lbs.
Green ballons can lift 2.5 lbs.
Blue balloons can lift 3 lbs.

Which balloons will you
need to lift exactly 11 lbs?

50. Lift-off!
What is the total weight
that this bunch of seven
balloons can lift?

11lbs

51. Action Ant!

The ant in the middle needs to reach one of the leaves without stepping over any black lines.

If you're one of those smarties who begins a maze at the end and works back to the start, you'll be stumped here!

With these combinations of weight,
the see-saw is perfectly balanced.

52. Teetering tower
Find the correct counterweight.

1.

2.

3.

4.

53. Shaky balance
Again, find the correct
counterbalance.

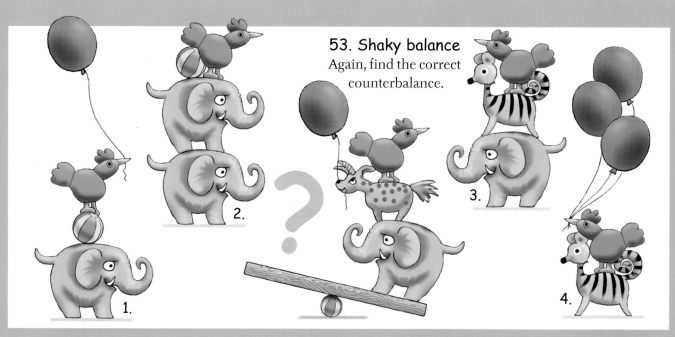

1.

2.

3.

4.

54. Tricky track
It should take you no
more than one minute
to find your way
through the
four stars.

55. Pick a paddle
Which paddle should
the girl pick up?

56. Short delivery
Each door has been freshly painted in the color of the house it belongs to.

But which one is missing?

57. Missing window
There's also a window missing—for which house?

58. Trapped butterfly
For one of the butterflies, there is no escape!

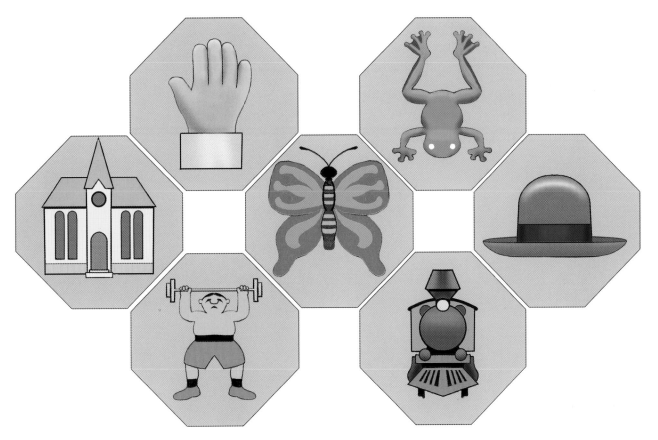

59. Odd one out Which of the above objects is out of place?

60. Marsmathics Work out the value of the symbols.
The first picture will get you going!

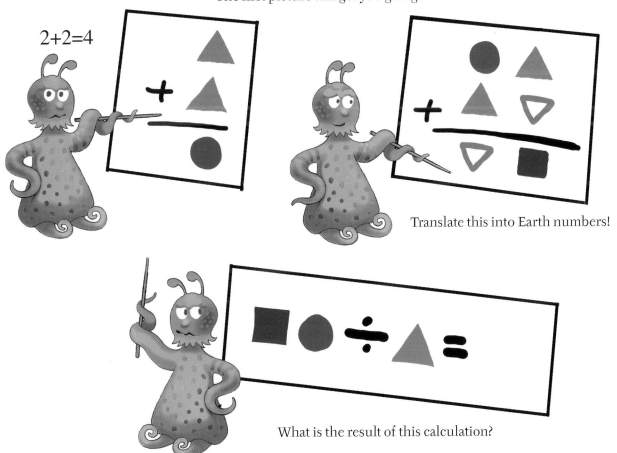

2+2=4

Translate this into Earth numbers!

What is the result of this calculation?

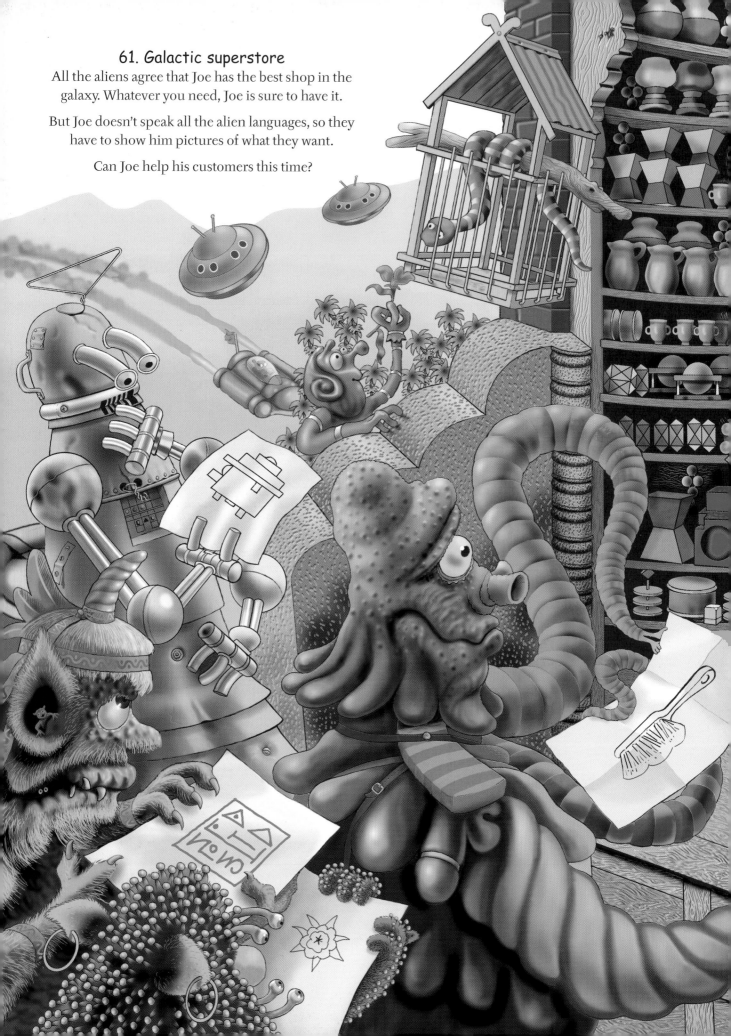

61. Galactic superstore

All the aliens agree that Joe has the best shop in the galaxy. Whatever you need, Joe is sure to have it.

But Joe doesn't speak all the alien languages, so they have to show him pictures of what they want.

Can Joe help his customers this time?

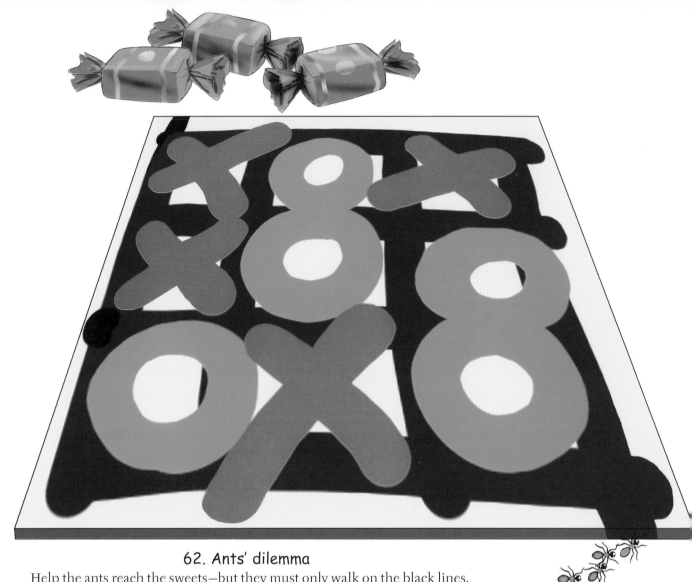

62. Ants' dilemma
Help the ants reach the sweets—but they must only walk on the black lines.

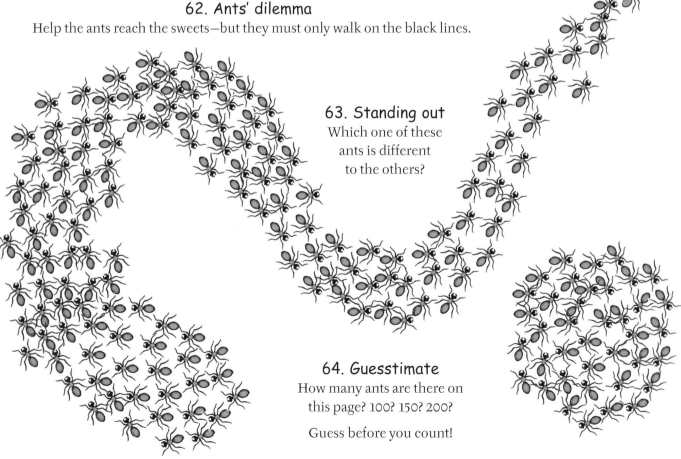

63. Standing out
Which one of these ants is different to the others?

64. Guesstimate
How many ants are there on this page? 100? 150? 200?

Guess before you count!

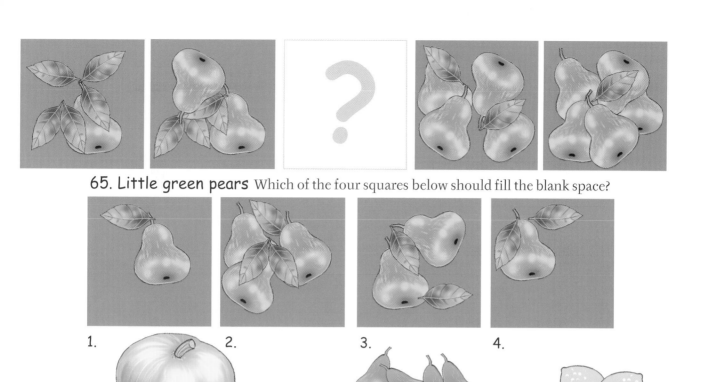

65. Little green pears Which of the four squares below should fill the blank space?

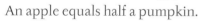

An apple equals half a pumpkin.

Four pears are worth one pumpkin.

Two lemons are worth two apples.

66. Value for money
Which of the six displays would cost the most?

67. Octodiscs Which of the four circles below belongs in the empty space?

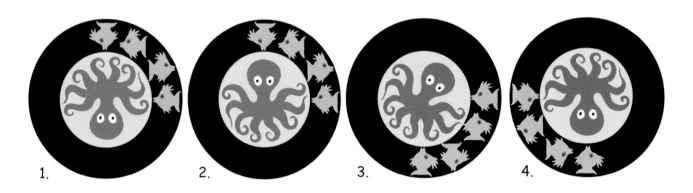

1.   2.   3.   4.

68. Danger!
Big-bellied silver cods are delicious—but those
with red eyes, green spots and forked tails are poisonous!

Are there any poisonous fish below?

69. Mutant amoeba
Do all of these amoebas look alike?

Check again—one is different.

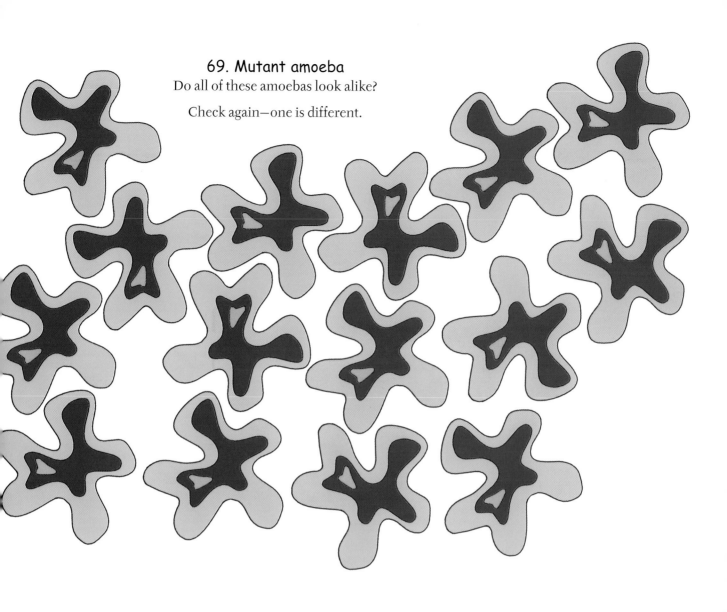

70. Untouchable bug
Which of these bugs is forever out of reach?

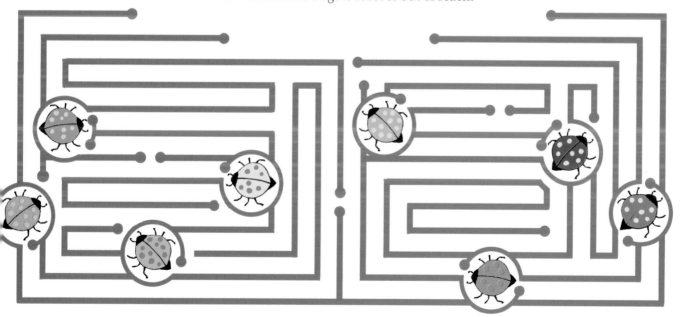

71. Look-alike pets

People and their pets often look alike!

Can you pick which animal belongs to whom?

72. Train your eyes
What number belongs
on the blue wagon?

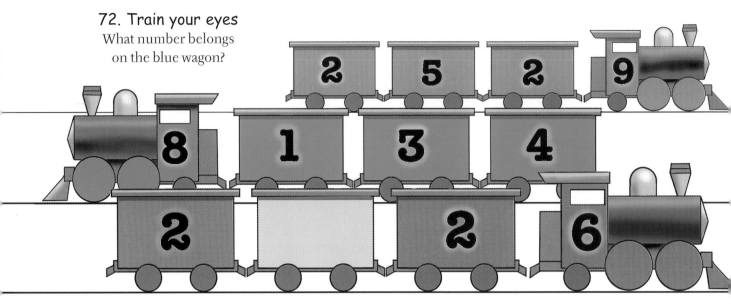

73. Follow that star!
Only one entrance will allow you
to reach the center of the maze.

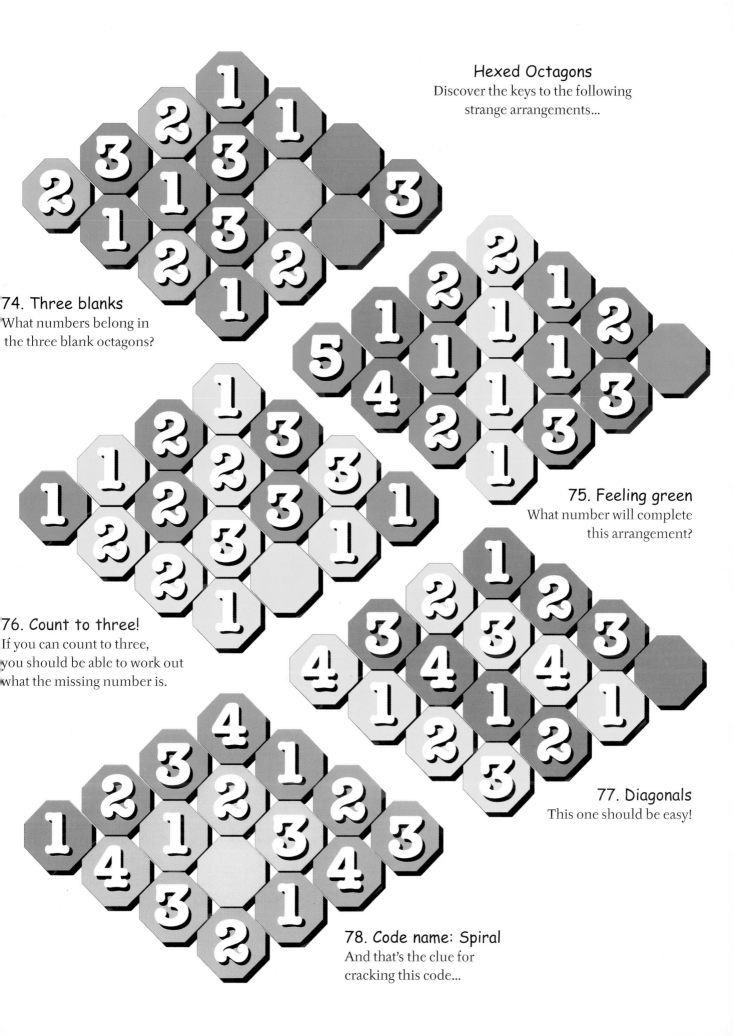

Hexed Octagons
Discover the keys to the following strange arrangements...

74. Three blanks
What numbers belong in the three blank octagons?

75. Feeling green
What number will complete this arrangement?

76. Count to three!
If you can count to three, you should be able to work out what the missing number is.

77. Diagonals
This one should be easy!

78. Code name: Spiral
And that's the clue for cracking this code...

1.

2.

3.

4.

5. .

6.

7.

8.

9.

10.

79. Flawed ruby
Which of these 10 rubies
is not like the others?

80. White diamond

81. Black diamond

82. Frogs and flowers Which of the six squares below belongs in the blank space?

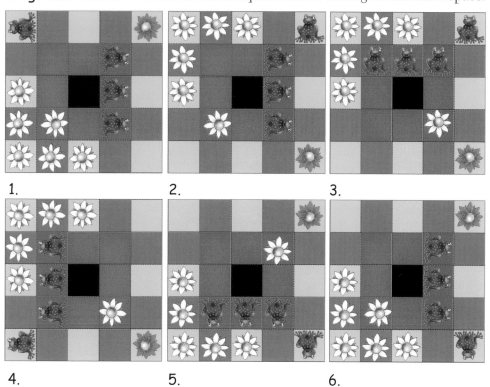

1.

2.

3.

4.

5.

6.

83. Cubic error This is supposed to be the same cube drawn from four different angles—but one of these pictures is wrong.

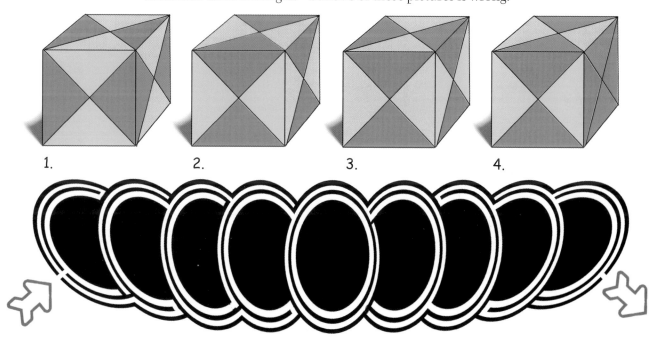

1.

2.

3.

4.

84. Frisky Frisbees

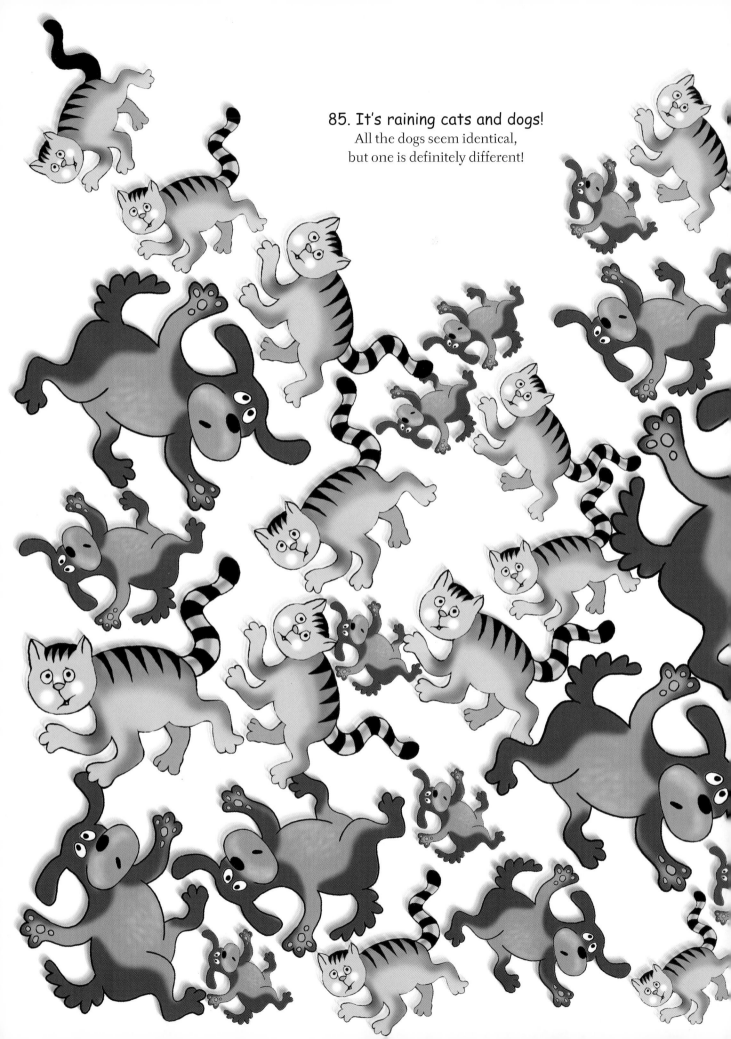

85. It's raining cats and dogs!
All the dogs seem identical,
but one is definitely different!

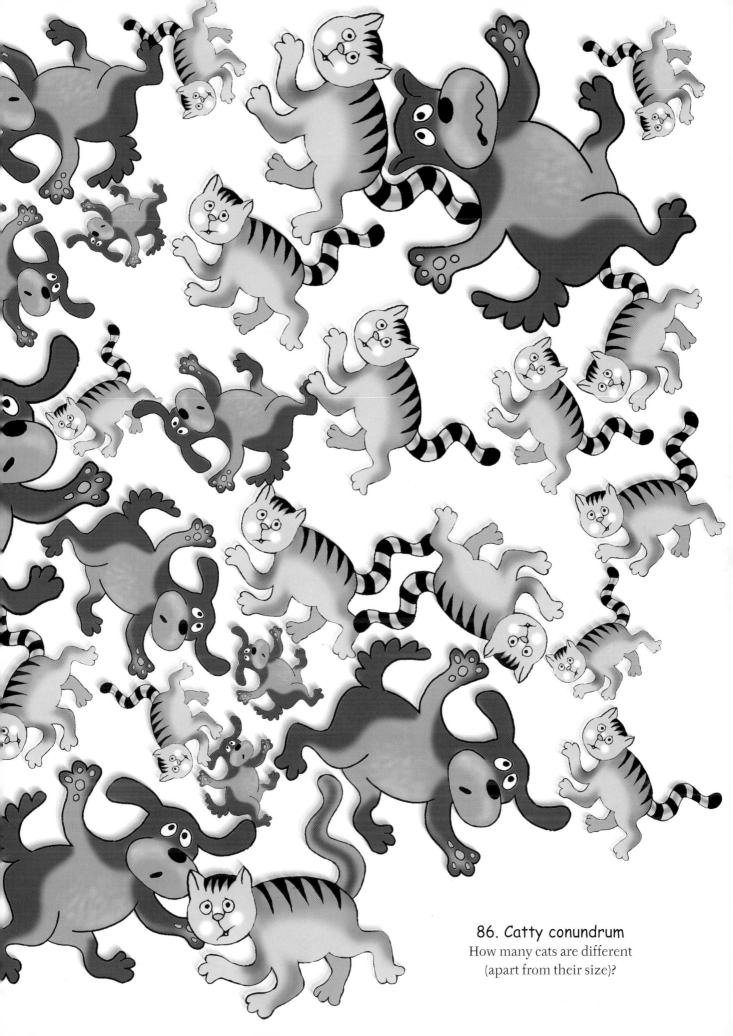

86. Catty conundrum
How many cats are different
(apart from their size)?

87. Clown beetles There are five varieties of clown beetles, but only four are represented in the collection above.

Can you spot the fifth variety?

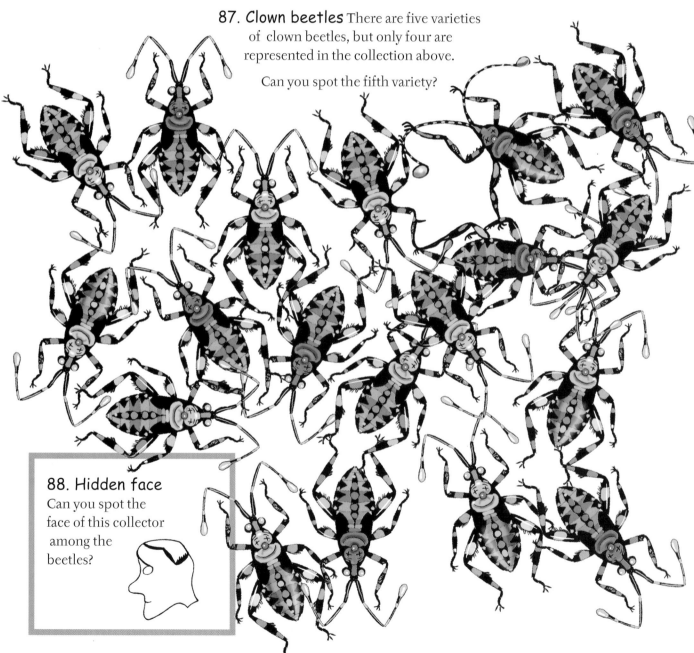

88. Hidden face
Can you spot the face of this collector among the beetles?

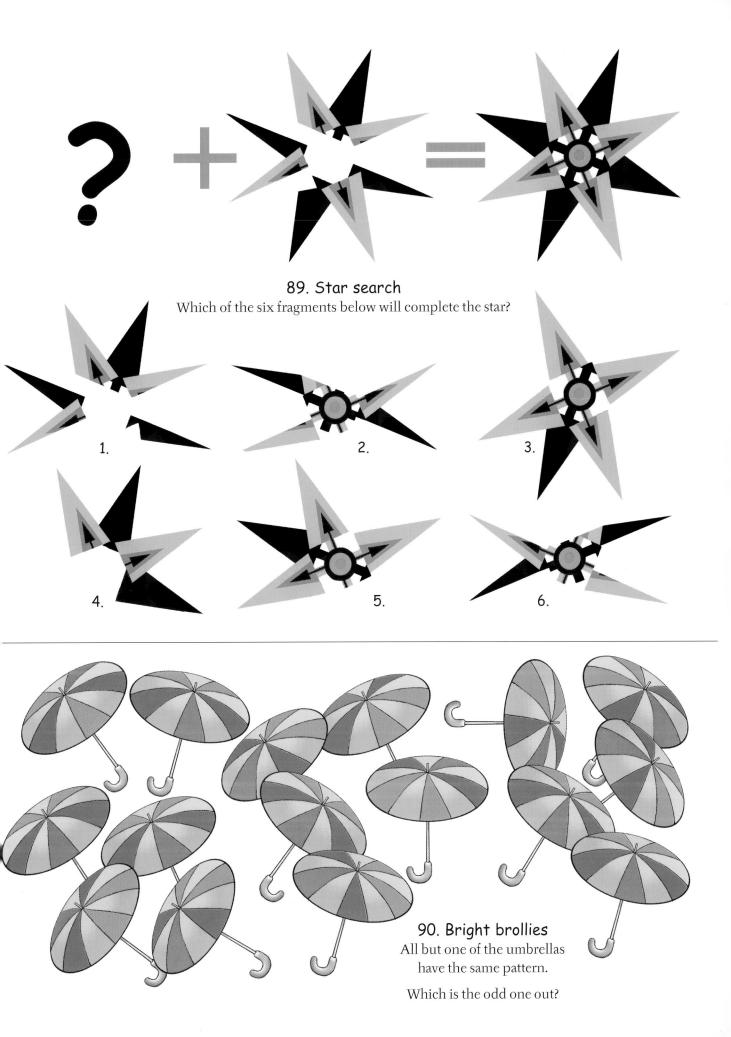

89. Star search
Which of the six fragments below will complete the star?

1.

2.

3.

4.

5.

6.

90. Bright brollies
All but one of the umbrellas
have the same pattern.

Which is the odd one out?

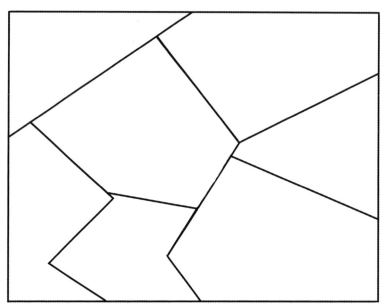

91. Shattered numbers

The house number on the above plate has been shattered.
Can you work out what the number was?

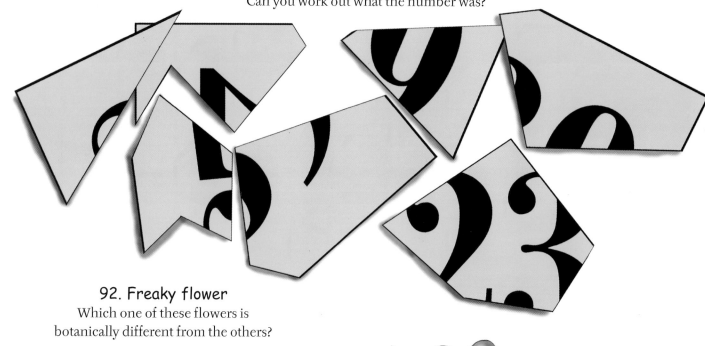

92. Freaky flower

Which one of these flowers is
botanically different from the others?

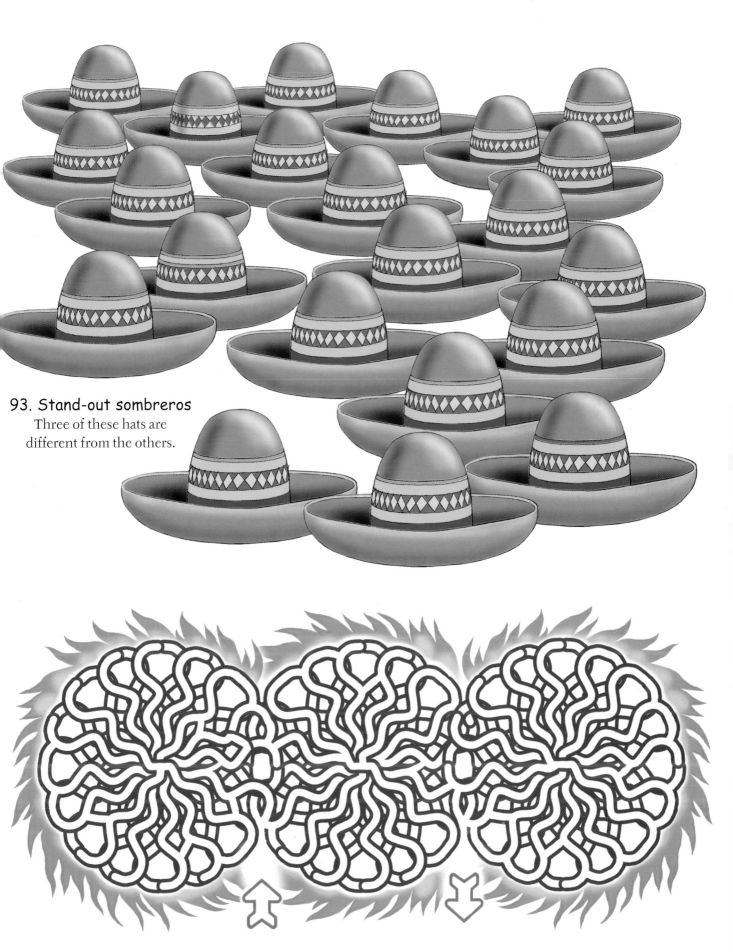

93. Stand-out sombreros
Three of these hats are different from the others.

94. Wheels of fire Get through them as fast as you can!

95. Snake-necked catpeckers

Snake-necked catpeckers are playful birds, and not at all vicious.
It should only take a little prod with a stick to free poor Sooty.

But which bird must the farmer prod?

96. Shape search

Find these five hidden shapes!

Solutions

1. **Gift-giving** Both gifts have the same value.
2. **Fruit Platter** In order of value: 6 (31 pts), 2 (23 pts), 5 (22 pts), 1 (17 pts), 4 (8 pts), 3 (7 pts)
3. **Lost sock** The diplomat needs a Royal Mark.
4. **Star-crossed snake**

5. **Giant leaf** Number 2 is the only one who can reach the center.

6. **Pillars of society** The topmost caterpillar has different spots.

7. **Apple turn-over** Each apple has turned 90° clockwise.

8. **Brush-rush** This maze is so easy you shouldn't even need a map!

9. **Double dragon trouble**

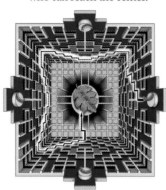

10. **Snail race** Diagram 4 is correct.
11. **Family reunion** The small snail on the bottom left with a yellow ribbon is the outsider—its shell spirals in a different direction.
12. **Three-in-a-row** The picture in the center is left over.
13. **Odd one out** The pirate only has one leg—everything else has four.
14. **Copied keys** The yellow key wasn't copied.
15. **Apple snakes** The purple snake has eaten two red and two green apples.

16. **Out of Reach**

17. **Butterfly friends** The two colored butterflies are exactly the same. The red spots on the others indicate their differences.

18. **Pilot error** Check the wing tips of the lowest plane.
19. **Double-checking double-deckers** The bottom plane on the right has a flash that goes UNDER the red band.
20. **Day-dreamers** Use your imagination! Here are some: bear, fish, dog, kangaroo, sleeping cat, elephant, crocodile, lizard, bird.

21. **Fantastic faces** You should see at least 15.
22. **House cat** The first cat on the left lives at number 5—the cats' spots are the same colors as the curtains, and their tails are on the same side as the chimneys.

23. **Cat and mouse**

24. **Special delivery** The brown parcel goes to house number 10.
25. **Flower arrangement** The flowerbox goes to house number 6.
26. **Cat city!** There are 25 cats.
27. **Golden delicious**

28. **Fractured star** Number 5 completes the star.

29. **Missing mandolin** Number 1 fits—the background color alternates, while the number of strings increases by one each time.

30. **Missed a spot!** Number 4 belongs in the missing section.

31. **Through the butterfly**

32. **Apple-loving grub**

33. **Tree of life**
The arrows indicate the three spots.

34. **Starry, starry jungle**

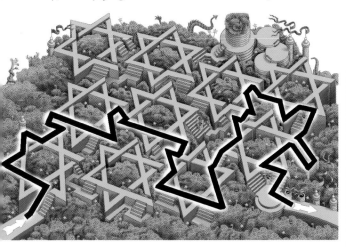

35. **Magic mandala**

36. **Odd one out** This is certainly not a heavenly body! All the others are...

37. **Color code**

38. **Shady deals**

39. **Odd objects**

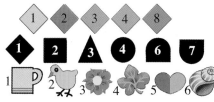

40. **All together now** The items in the big box add up to 59.

41. **Odd one out** It's the plane, of course! (It's not a musical instrument.)

42. **Vanishing violin case**

43. **Notable error**
The last bar has an extra ⅛ note.

44. **Spiders' nest**
There are only 21 of these spiders, so they must be male.

There are 25 of these spiders, so they must be female.

45. **Colored kites** The answer is number 7. (The colors of the tail always advance one place.)

46. **Giddy geckos** Most geckos have green hind feet, except those who will be able to find their way to the middle.

47. **Kite-flying competition**
These two children didn't dress in the colors of their kites.

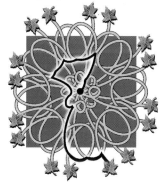

48. **Personal judgement**
There's no right answer— it's just personal choice!

49. **Super balloons** Two blue balloons can lift 6 lbs, and two green ones can lift 5. The total is 11 lbs.

50. **Lift-off!** The total weight they can lift is 28 lbs.

51. **Action Ant!**

52. **Teetering tower** Number 1 will balance the see-saw.

53. **Shaky balance**
Number 1 will balance the see-saw.

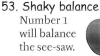

54. **Tricky track**

55. Pick a paddle The paddles should add up to the number on her sweater.

56. Short delivery The door for number 8 is missing.

57. Missing window One of the windows for number 12 is missing.

58. Trapped butterfly The blue butterfly is trapped forever!

59. Odd one out The hand is the only object which is not symmetrical.

60. Marsmathics 2+2=4; 42+26=68; 84÷2=42

61. Galactic superstore

62. Ants' dilemma

63. Standing out The first ant has a blue body.

64. Guesstimate There are 186 ants in the picture.

65. Little green pears Number 2 is correct, with 3 pears and 3 leaves. (The number of pears in the top row increases by one, while the leaves decrease by one.)

66. Value for money The pears are clearly the cheapest. If we give each item a numerical value, pear=1; pumpkin=4; apple=2; lemon=2. So, square 1=15; 2=16; 3=6; 4=11; 5=21; 6=18. Square 5 is worth the most.

67. Octodiscs Disc number 4 is the best fit. Each octopus turns 90° clockwise, while the outer rim turns 90° counter-clockwise.

68. Danger! There is one poisonous fish!

69. Mutant amoeba This is the only different one.

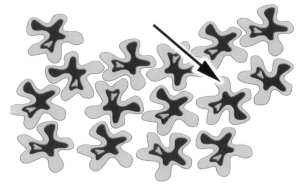

70. Untouchable bug The green-and-red bug can't be reached.

71. Look-alike pets Follow the black lines.

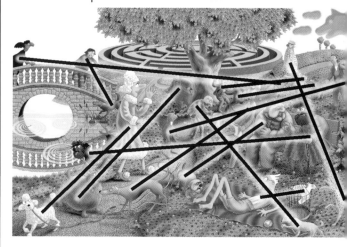

72. Train your eyes The number 2 belongs on the blue wagon. (The wagons add up to the number in the locomotive.)

73. Follow that star!

74. **Three blanks** Blue octagons are 1, red octagons are 3, orange octagons are 2.

75. **Feeling green** Each vertical column adds up to 5.

76. **Count to three!** Reading horizontally, the numbers 1, 2 and 3 are repeated. The blank space needs a 3.

77. **Diagonals** All the diagonals add up to 10, so the blank space needs a 4.

78. **Code name: Spiral** If you start from the left side and go clockwise, the numbers 1, 2, 3 and 4 are repeated in a spiral. The blank space needs a 4.

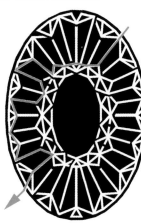

79. **Flawed ruby** Number 6 is different.

80. **White diamond**   81. **Black diamond**

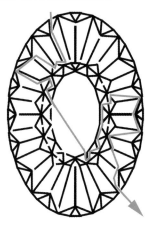

82. **Frogs and flowers** Number 1 belongs in the blank space. The inner row of red squares turns 90° counter-clockwise, while the outer row turns 90° clockwise.

83. **Cubic error** Number 4 is wrong. (Opposite sides are always the same.)

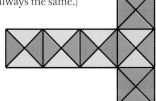

84. **Frisky frisbees**

85. **It's raining cats and dogs!** and

86. **Catty conundrum** Three cats are different from the others.

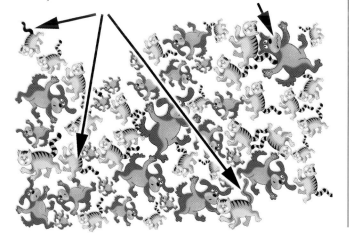

87. **Clown beetles** and

88. **Hidden face** The colored beetle is the fifth variety. The white area marks the face.

89. **Star search** Number 2 completes the star.

90. **Bright brollies** The umbrella in the top left corner is different.

91. **Shattered numbers**

92. **Freaky flower** This flower has six petals instead of five.

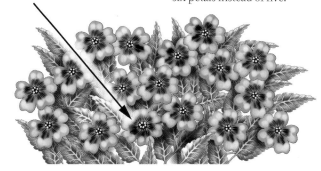

93. **Stand-out sombreros** These hats are different.

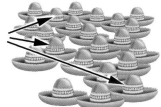

94. **Wheels of fire**

95. **Snake-necked catpeckers** and

96. **Shape search**

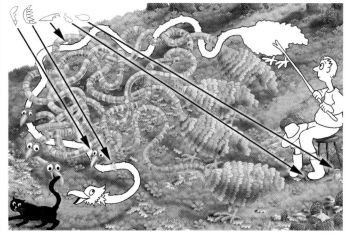

ROLF HEIMANN'S
PUZZLE MANIA

Perplexing puzzles & maddening mazes

I can't believe that Earth is the only planet in the universe that harbors life. After all, there are billions of stars!

But what might these other life forms look like, and what kinds of lives do they lead? Will they be intelligent? And how should we test their intelligence?

Giving them a copy of *Puzzlemania* would be a good start. If they can do most of the puzzles in this book, I'd class them as intelligent!

Quick getaway

The volcano is exploding!
Help the astronauts get back to the spaceship
before all the paths are blocked by falling rocks.

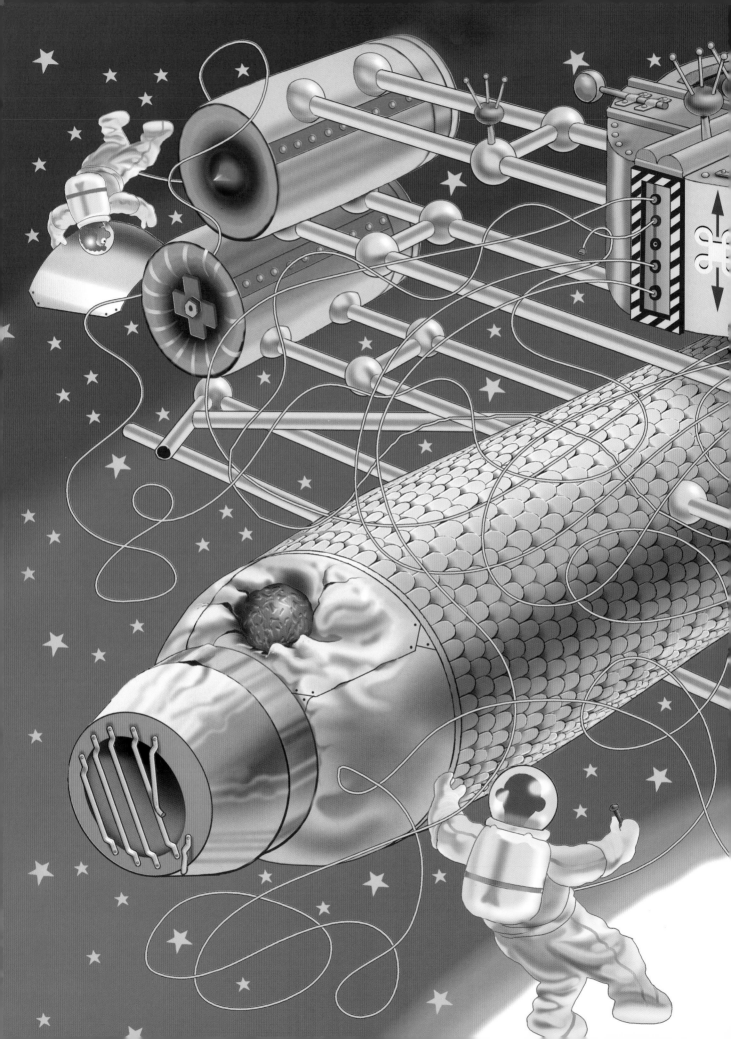

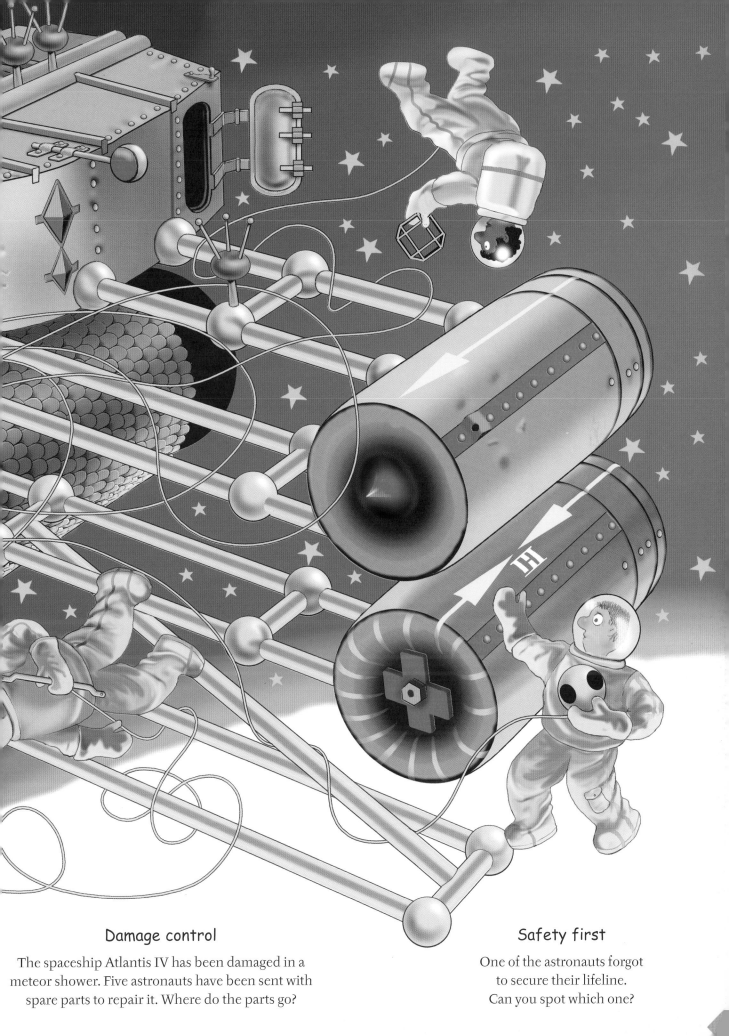

Damage control

The spaceship Atlantis IV has been damaged in a
meteor shower. Five astronauts have been sent with
spare parts to repair it. Where do the parts go?

Safety first

One of the astronauts forgot
to secure their lifeline.
Can you spot which one?

Where's my baby?

Mrs Pinkapp has picked up her baby from the crèche, but Mrs Bluetopp is still looking for hers! Can you find it?

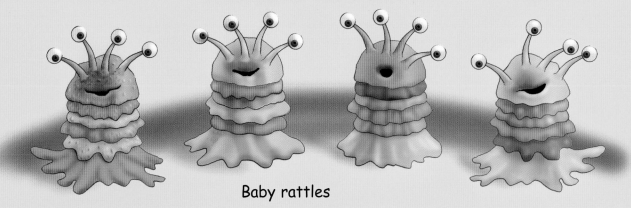

Baby rattles

Calamarian babies insist that the colors of
their rattles match their own colors.
Can you find the rattles belonging to these babies?

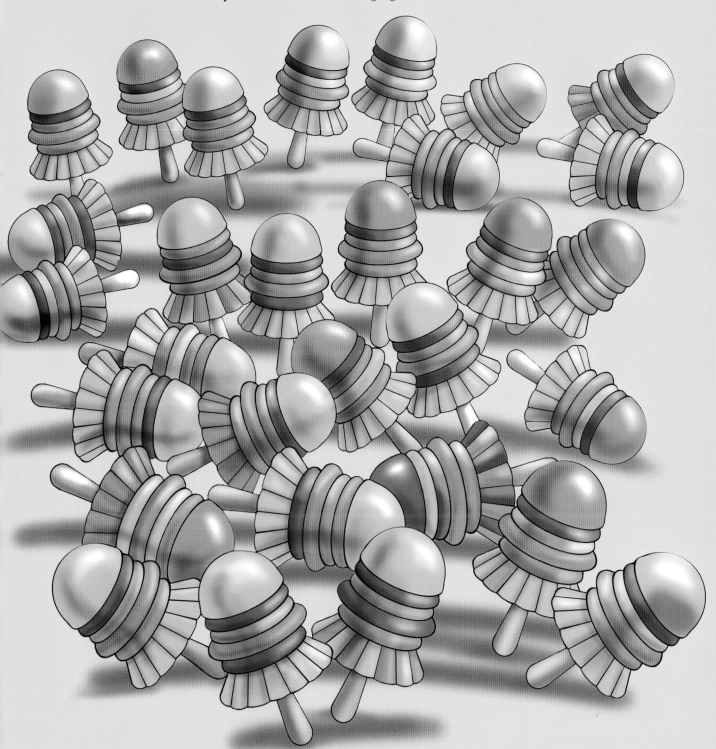

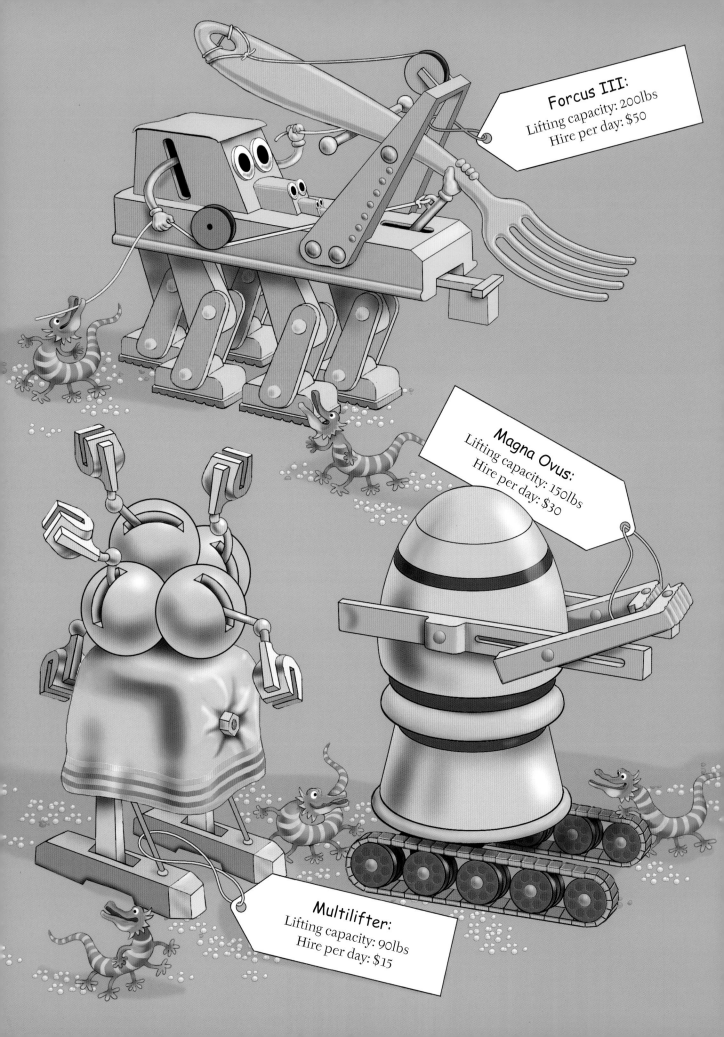

Forcus III:
Lifting capacity: 200lbs
Hire per day: $50

Magna Ovus:
Lifting capacity: 150lbs
Hire per day: $30

Multilifter:
Lifting capacity: 90lbs
Hire per day: $15

The amazing gogophant!

This gogophant weighs 356 lbs. A number of lifters must be
hired to transport it. Which is the cheapest option?

Missing tiles

Eight tiles have fallen from the Dragon Temple of Xarapoon, but only seven of them can be found. Which one is missing?

Martian IQ test

Which of the five signs below fits
into the blank panel?

is to

is to

as

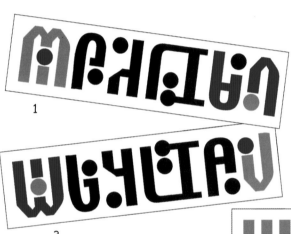

1

3

5

4

Symmetry first

Which one of the five figures below
should go into the empty space?

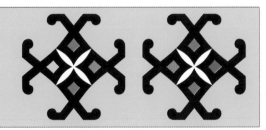

1   2   3   4   5

Robot alert

Go in one antenna and out the other!

The original

Master Yellowburg has built an original maze—and he doesn't want it to be copied. Can you find your way through?

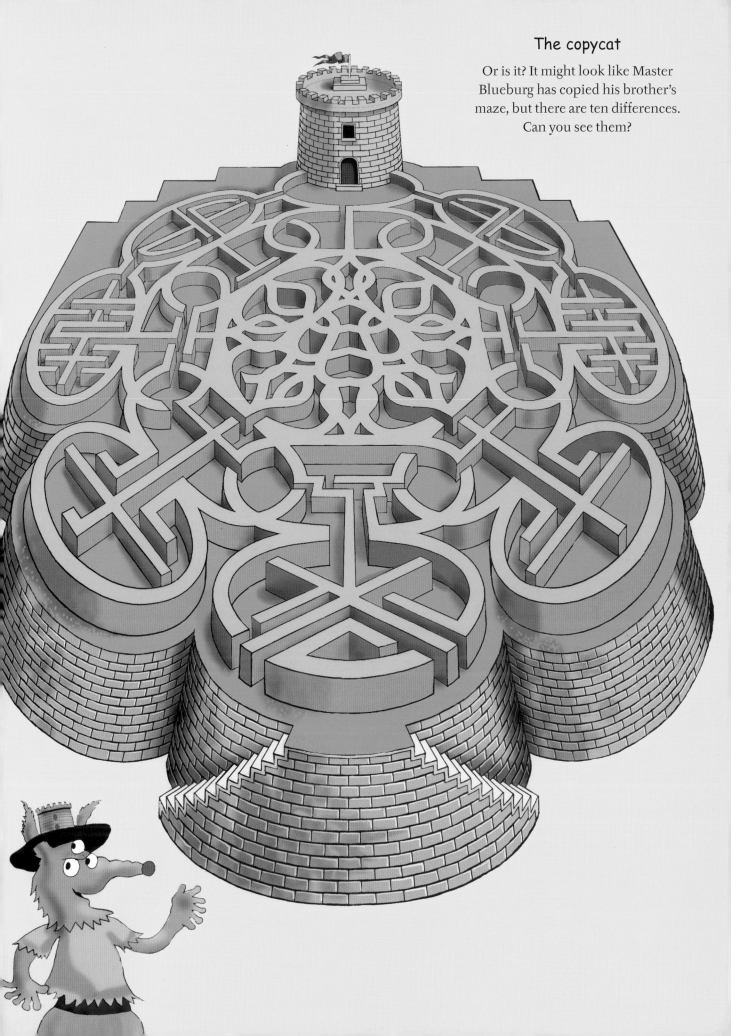

The copycat

Or is it? It might look like Master Blueburg has copied his brother's maze, but there are ten differences. Can you see them?

Good things come in fives!

At least that's what the five-toothed inhabitants of
the planet Pentalus think! You can't see their teeth,
but there are plenty of other things that come in fives.
How many can you find?

Petwalk

Four ladies from Canopus III are taking their pets for a walk, but the boisterous animals are running wild. Which pet belongs to whom?

Spacemaze!

Navigate your way from top to bottom of this spacemaze without leaving the white line.

Star wall

Which of these five stars fits into the empty space on the wall?

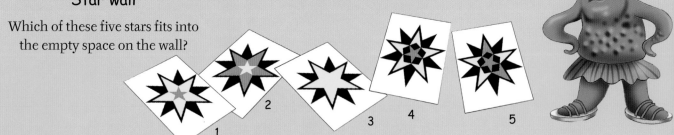

1   2   3   4   5

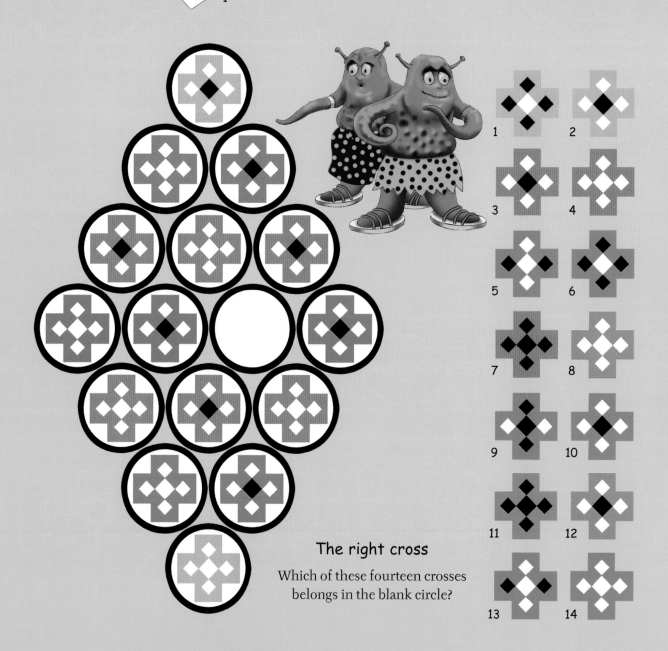

The right cross

Which of these fourteen crosses belongs in the blank circle?

1   2

3   4

5   6

7   8

9   10

11   12

13   14

Black star

Only one of the eight entrances
will lead you to the star in the center.
Mind you don't step over any black lines!
(The critter on the right is giving you a clue...)

The Mirror of Lies

The shopping mall of Satrunus is having a competition.
Customers who spot all 10 things which the Mirror of Lies
reflects wrongly will win a free tentacle trim. You could too!

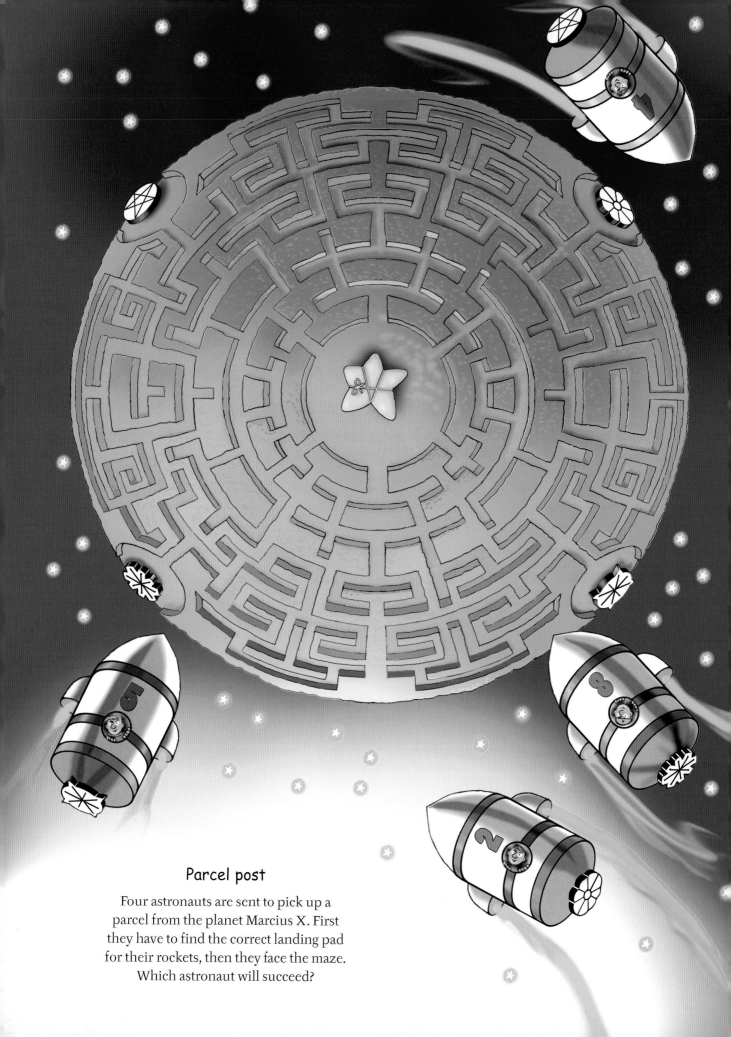

Parcel post

Four astronauts are sent to pick up a parcel from the planet Marcius X. First they have to find the correct landing pad for their rockets, then they face the maze. Which astronaut will succeed?

Planet of the Moles

The people of Tunnelius have riddled their planet with tunnels so that they can go from day to night and from dawn to dusk without ever setting foot on the surface. Can you do the same?

Spot the spot

Can you find the spot where
this flowerpot belongs?

Wild cats

Round up the 12 Ring-tailed
Lobocats, or no flowerpot is safe!

Star walk

Leave by one path and
return by another.

Postcards from Calacaroo

The stamps on two of these
postcards are counterfeit.
Can you see which two, and why?

Solutions

Quick getaway

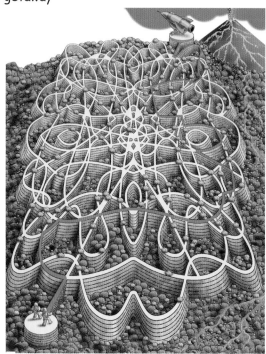

Baby rattles

The amazing gogophant! Hire four multilifters. Together they will lift 360 lbs at a cost of $60 per day.

Missing tiles This one is missing!

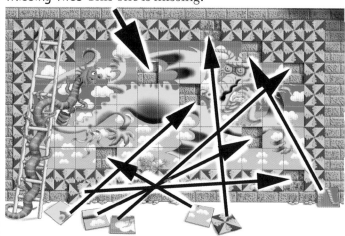

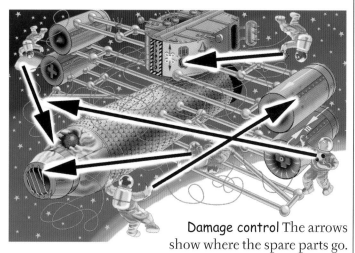

Damage control The arrows show where the spare parts go.

Safety first The astronaut in the top-left corner is not connected.

Martian IQ test Panel number 2 fits—the sign is mirror-reversed, but the order of colors stays the same.

Symmetry first Figure number 5 fits. It is the only one which keeps the yellow panel symmetrical.

Robot alert

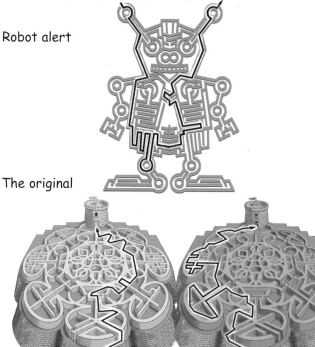

The original

Where's my baby?

Here!

The copycat The red circles mark the ten differences.

Good things come in fives!

There are 5 hills, 5 towers, 5 bridges (one with 5 arches, and one with 5 supports), 5 railway cars with 5 windows each, 5 rockets, 5 five-legged Pentalus geese, 5 five-legged Pentalus oxen pulling a wagon with 5 axles, 5 urns, 5 snakes, 5 yellow flowers, 5 bull rushes, 5 robots, 5 forks, 5 rugs, 5 five-striped pentalopes, 5 blue flags, 5 purple flowers and a roundabout marking the junction of 5 streets. Maybe you can even find more fives?

Parcel post Number 5 will deliver the parcel.

Planet of the Moles

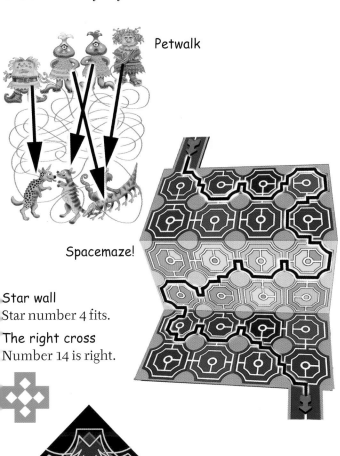

Petwalk

Spacemaze!

Star wall
Star number 4 fits.

The right cross
Number 14 is right.

Spot the spot
The arrow shows where the flowerpot has to go.

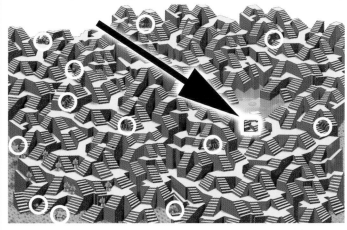

Wild cats
The circles show the position of the 12 cats.

Star walk

Black star
Follow path number 5.

Postcards from Calacaroo

These two stamps are different. (On one the tentacle goes in front instead of behind, and on the other the lettering is mirror-reversed.)

The Mirror of Lies
Black circles indicate false reflections.

Beetle reunion

Will these two beetles be able to meet? With your help they will!

Brothers in arms

Lorax is to his brother Xarol...

As Tiger is to his brother...

?

Temple teaser

Find your way through the maze to the temple.

Escape from the castle

Can you escape from the castle's turret?

Wrong window

There are 20 windows in the castle, all the same—except one. Can you spot which one?

Faulty flag

One of the flags is wrong, too!

Tricky squares

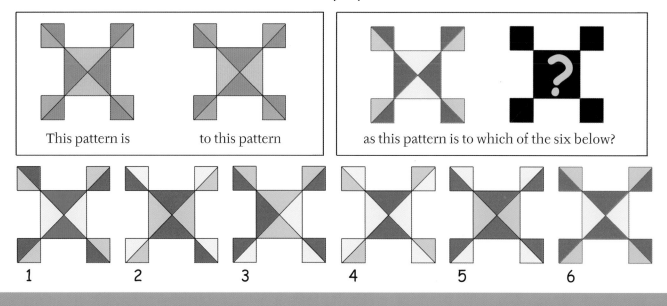

This pattern is   to this pattern   as this pattern is to which of the six below?

1   2   3   4   5   6

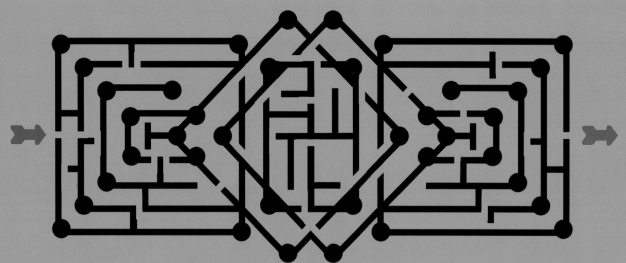

Easy come, easy go

This might look like an easy maze—but don't be deceived!

Diamonds are forever

But don't take forever to find which gem fits the blank space below!

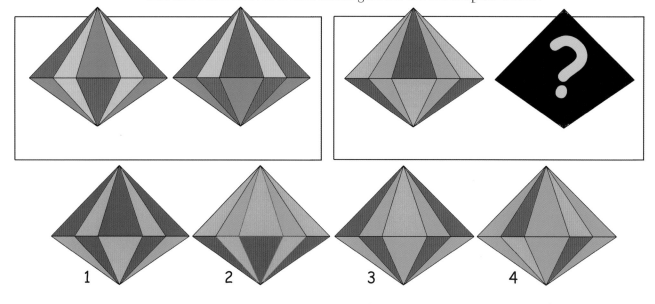

1   2   3   4

Lucky bug
Only one of these bugs can reach the flower.
Which one?

Ship ahoy!

If you want to get into the lifeboat that belongs to this ship, you'd better look closely—
which one of the boats in the water should you choose?

Trapped

Help the yellow fish
out of the maze and
into the open sea!

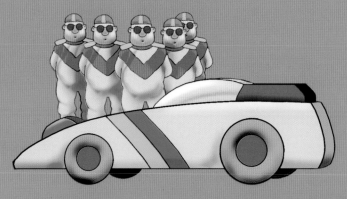

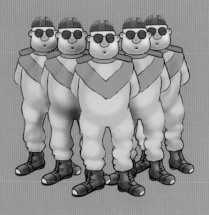

Pit stop problem

The uniforms of the pit stop crew match the cars they service.
Which of the six cars below is the one for the waiting team?

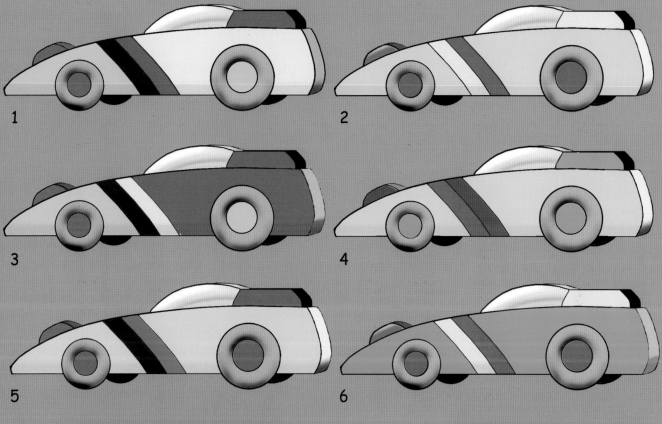

1

2

3

4

5

6

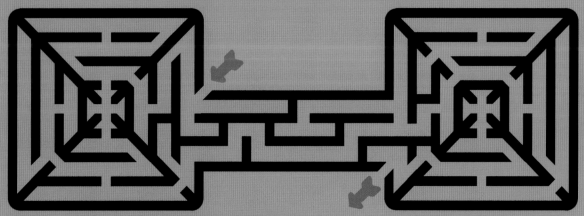

Be quick!

If you can do this maze in 30 seconds flat, you'll be a hit with the pit stop crew!

Lend a hand!

The whole maze has to be
painted blue, so grab a brush
and find your way to the last
bit of yellow.

Two of a kind
Though their sizes may differ, two of the fish in the school above resemble each other exactly.

What color is the ball in my hand?

An educated guess
After studying the number of balls on the table, can you guess the color of the ball in the man's hand?

Sail away

What numbers should go on the pink hull, and on the reefed sail of the last ship?

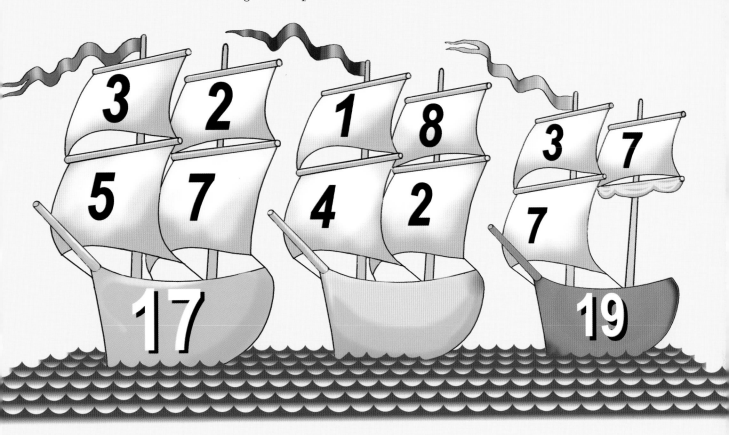

Paper flotilla

Only one of these paper boats was made of the paper on which the flotilla sits.

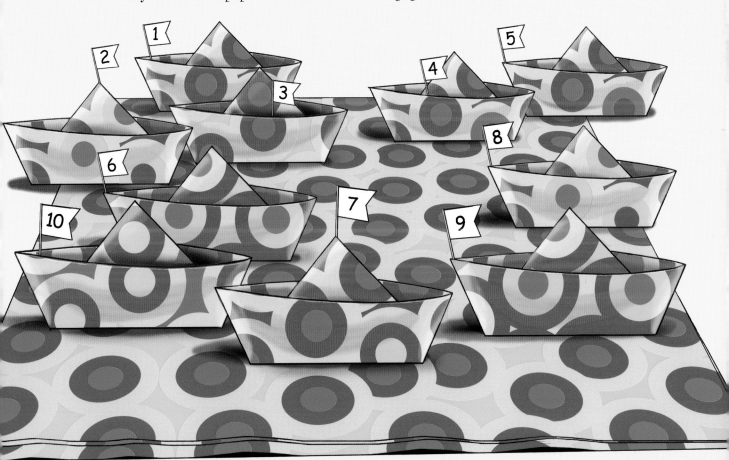

Day 1 Day 2 Day 3 Day 4 Day 5 Day 6 Day 7 **?** Day 8 Day 9 Day 10

Changing flowers

The floral arrangement is changed according to a regular system—
every day a new flower is added, but each flower only lasts three days before it is removed.
What would the arrangement look like on Day 7?

1   2   3   4   5   6

Wheels within wheels
You might get dizzy going through this maze, but don't give up!

Upstairs, downstairs
It's a long way from the lake to the flower garden—
especially with all those stairs to climb!

Wall art
An artist has taken a lot of care to paint the correct emblem of the Gardeners' Guild on the walls. He only made one mistake...Can you spot it?

Lure of the lily

Love lilies are a delicacy for red-backed beetles.
Which one of these four will reach the prize?

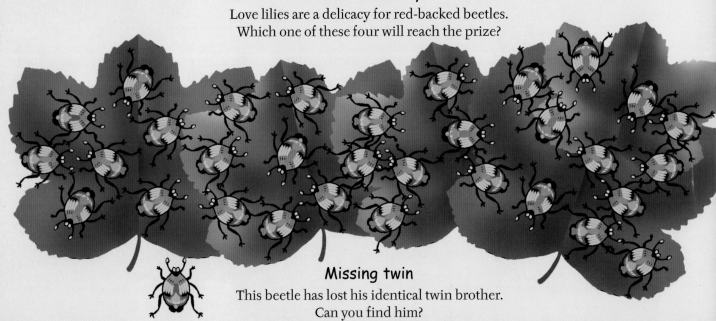

Missing twin

This beetle has lost his identical twin brother.
Can you find him?

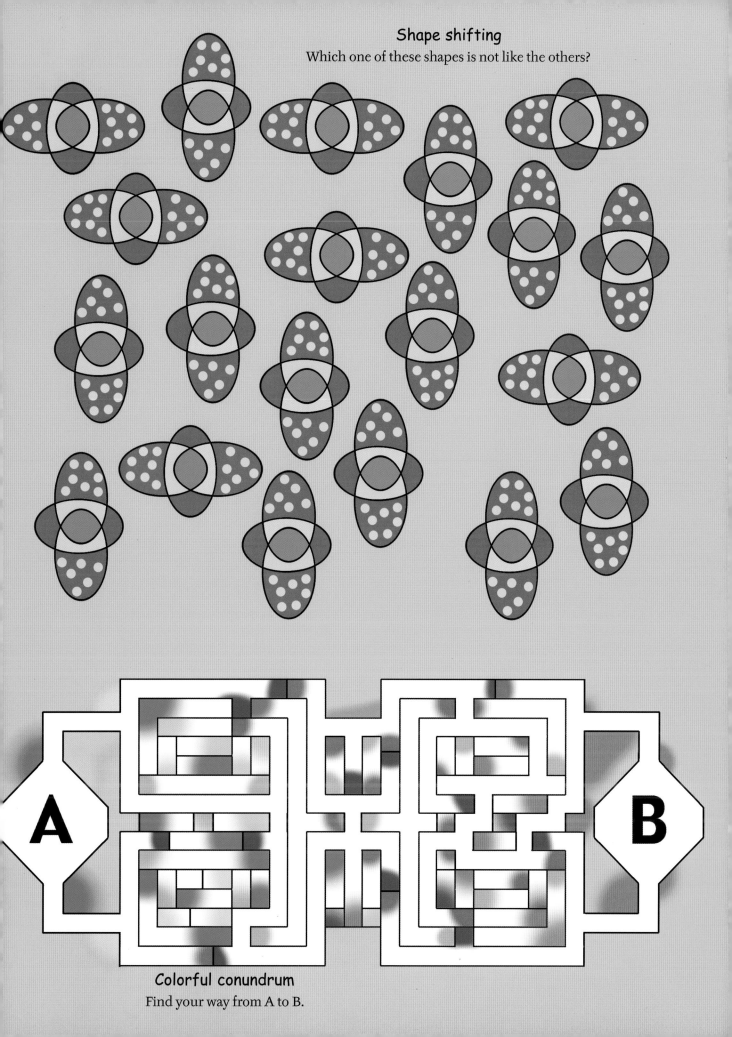

Shape shifting
Which one of these shapes is not like the others?

Colorful conundrum
Find your way from A to B.

Wiggly worries

These three children are looking for their pet snake, Rover. Can you help them?

He has red eyes

...and a red tail

...and red spots all over.

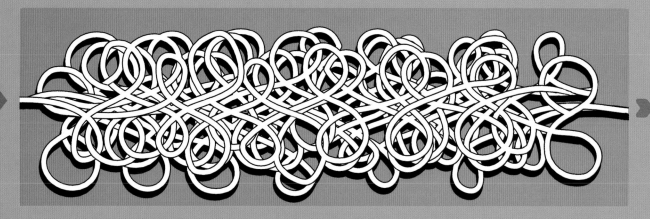

Tangled twine
Don't cross any black lines!

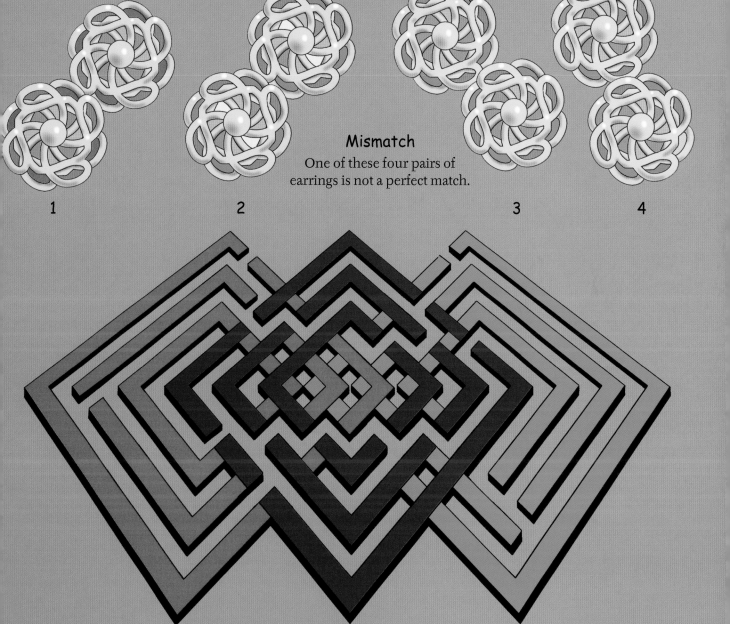

Mismatch
One of these four pairs of
earrings is not a perfect match.

1

2

3

4

Easy breezy
Try this maze—it's a breeze!

Gone fishing

Some people will go to any length to find a good fishing spot! Help this fisherman through the maze to the fishpond.

Snake tails

How many snakes are on this page? Sometimes the tails are all you can see!

Mystery shards

Which of the ten shapes below fits the blank space in the figure to the right? (Rotate the shape if necessary!)

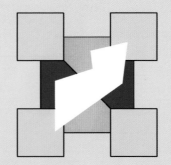

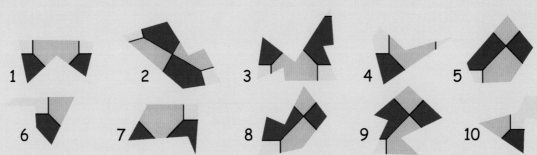

1 2 3 4 5
6 7 8 9 10

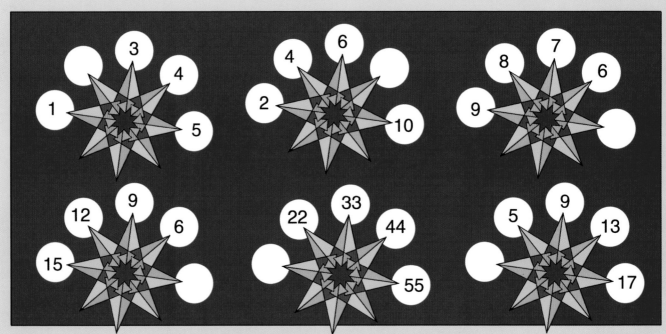

Dodge the confetti
Keep to the white lines!

Star system
Filling in the blanks is easy—just follow the system!

Target practice

Each of the four competitors in the archery competition has their own kind of arrow. Who won?

The shivering seven

Nothing, not even freezing temperatures, will stop the
seven gentlemen of the Polar Bear Club from having
their weekly swim—except if they forget their towels!
Which of the Polar Bears has forgotten his towel today?

Pieces of eight

Now try to find the eight shapes below
hidden in the picture!

Solutions

Beetle reunion

Brothers in arms
As Tiger is to his brother
Regit

Temple teaser

Escape from the castle
Wrong window
Faulty flag

Tricky squares
Number 6

Easy come, easy go

Diamonds are forever
Number 2

Lucky bug

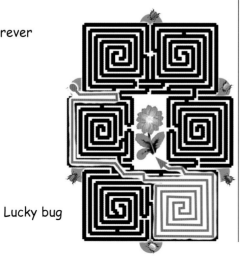

Ship ahoy
Trapped

Pit stop problem
Number 4

Be quick!

Lend a hand!

Two of a kind

An educated guess
A pink ball. There
are 10 balls of every
other color, but only
nine pink balls.

Sail away
The numbers on the sails
add up to the number on
the hull.

Paper flotilla
Number 3

Changing flowers
Number 4

Wheels within wheels

Upstairs downstairs

Wall art

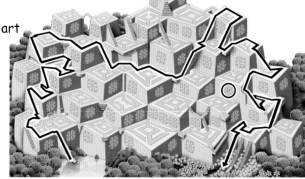

Lure of the lily

Missing twin

Shape shifting
The shape in the
top left-hand
corner is different.

Colorful conundrum

Wiggly worries

Tangled twine

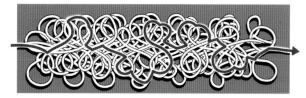

Mismatch
Number 4

Gone fishing
Snake tails

Mystery shards
Number 2

Dodge the confetti

Star system

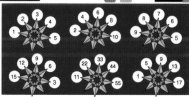

Target practice
Tina has 11 points, Liz has 10, Bob has 9 and Ted has 5.

The shivering seven
Pieces of eight

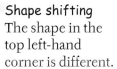

Rolf Heimann was born in Dresden, Germany in 1940. In 1945, he witnessed the total destruction of his home city—which made him a lifelong opponent of war.

At age 18 he migrated to Australia. Over the next few years he worked his way around the country doing all kinds of jobs, including fruit-picking, laboring at railways and working in factories. Every spare hour was spent writing and sketching. Eventually, he settled in Melbourne, where he worked for printers and publishers before finally running his own art studio.

In 1974, Rolf sailed his own boat around the Pacific (and met his future wife, Lila, in Samoa), returning to Australia after two years to concentrate on painting, writing, cartooning and illustrating. He has now published over twenty books of puzzles and mazes, several junior novels and a picture book. His books have travelled to dozens of countries, and have sold millions of copies around the world.

Little Hare Books
4/21 Mary Street, Surry Hills
NSW 2010 AUSTRALIA

www.littleharebooks.com

Rolf Heimann's Brain Busting Bonanza first published in 2003 (ISBN 1 877003 21 2)
Crazy Cosmos first published in 2004 (ISBN 1 877003 41 7)
Puzzlemazia first published in 2004 (ISBN 1 877003 64 6)
Copyright this edition © Rolf Heimann 2005

First published in 2005

National Library of Australia
Cataloguing-in-Publication entry

Heimann, Rolf, 1940- .
Rolf's crazy capers.

For children.
ISBN 1 877003 89 1 (pbk.)

1. Maze puzzles - Juvenile literature. 2. Puzzles -
Juvenile literature. I. Title.

793.73

Designed by ANTART
Printed in China
Produced by Phoenix Offset

2 4 5 3 1